the music
glee

season one

D0808883

volume 1

Wise Publications
part of The Music Sales Group
London / New York / Paris / Sydney / Copenhagen / Berlin / Madrid / Hong Kong / Tokyo

Published by
Wise Publications
14-15 Berners Street, London W1T 3LJ, UK.

Exclusive distributors:
Music Sales Limited
Distribution Centre,
Newmarket Road, Bury St Edmunds, Suffolk, IP33 3YB, UK.
Music Sales Pty Limited
20 Resolution Drive, Caringbah, NSW 2229, Australia.

Order No. AM1000450
ISBN 978-1-84938-512-1

Edited by Jenni Wheeler.

Printed in the EU.

www.musicsales.com

Your Guarantee of Quality

As publishers, we strive to produce every book to the highest
commercial standards. The music has been freshly engraved and
the book has been carefully designed to minimise awkward page
turns and to make playing from it a real pleasure.

Particular care has been given to specifying acid-free, neutral-sized
paper made from pulps which have not been elemental chlorine bleached.

This pulp is from farmed sustainable forests and was
produced with special regard for the environment.

Throughout, the printing and binding have been planned to ensure a sturdy,
attractive publication which should give years of enjoyment.

If your copy fails to meet our high standards, please inform us
and we will gladly replace it.

www.musicsales.com

Don't Stop Believin'

Words & Music by Steve Perry, Neal Schon
& Jonathan Cain

5

2. A sing-er in a smo-key room, the smell of wine and cheap per-fume.

For a smile they can share the night. It goes on and on___ and on___ and on.___

6

Don't stop be-liev-in'. Hold on to that feel-ing.

Street-light peo-ple. Oh.

Repeat ad lib. to fade

9

Can't Fight This Feeling

Words & Music by Kevin Cronin

11

and dark win-ter's night. And I'm get-ting clos-er than I

ev - er thought I might. And I can't fight this feel -

- ing an - y - more. I've for-got-ten what I

start-ed fight-ing for. It's time to bring this ship

14

Gold Digger

Words & Music by Ray Charles, Kanye West
& Richard Renald

leave.) (Yeah,— she give me mon - ey when I'm in need.)_

(She give me mon - ey when I'm in need.)_

(I got - ta leave.) (I got - ta

leave.) (I got - ta leave.) (I got - ta

leave.) (Yeah,__ she give me mon - ey when I'm in need.)__
Now I ain't say-in' she a gold dig- ger,

__ (She give me mon - ey when I'm in need.)__
but she ain't mess- in' wit' no broke, broke. Now I ain't say-in' she a gold dig- ger,

__ (I got-ta leave.) (I got-ta
but she ain't mess- in' wit' no broke, broke. Get down, girl, go 'head, get down.

leave.)   (I got-ta leave.)   (I got-ta
Get down, girl,   go 'head, get down.   Get down, girl,   go 'head, get down.

A♭7

leave.)   (Yeah,— she give me mon–)
Get down, girl,   go 'head.   *Rap 3 (See Additional Lyrics)*

D♭7

leave.) (Yeah,_ she give me mon - ey.)
Get down, girl, go 'head.

Additional Lyrics

Rap 1 Cutie the bomb, met her at a beauty salon
With a baby Louis Vuitton under her underarm.
She said, "I can tell you ROC, I can tell by your charm.
Far as girls, you got a flock; I can tell by your charm and your arm."
But I'm looking for the one, have you seen her?
My psychic told me she, yeah, have a ass like Serena,
Trina, Jennifer Lopez, four kids and I
Gotta take all their bad ass to showbiz?

Okay, get your kids, but then they got their friends.
I pulled up in the Benz, they all got up in.
We all went to din, and then I had to pay.
If you ******* with this girl, then you better be paid.
You know why? It take too much to touch her.
From what I heard, she got a baby by Busta.
My best friend said she used to **** with Usher.
I don't care what none of y'all say, I still love her.

Rap 2 Eighteen years, eighteen years.
She got one of your kids, got you for eighteen years.
I know somebody paying child support for one of his kids.
His baby mamma car and crib is bigger than his.
You will see him on TV any given Sunday,
Win the Superbowl and drive off in a Hyundai.
She was s'posed to buy your shorty TYCO with your money;
She went to the doctor, got lipo with your money.

She walking 'round looking like Michael with your money.
Should'a got that insured GEICO for your money
(Money). If you ain't no punk, holla
"We want prenup!" (We want prenup, yeah!)
It's something that you need to have,
'Cause when she leave yo ass, she gon' leave with half.
Eighteen years, eighteen years,
And on her eighteenth birthday he found out it wasn't his!?

Rap 3 Now I ain't sayin' you a gold digger; you got needs.
You don't want a dude to smoke, but he can't buy weed.
You go out to eat, he can't pay, y'all can't leave.
There's dishes in the back; he gotta roll up his sleeves,
But while y'all washin', watch him.
He gon' make it to a Benz out of that Datsun.
He got that ambition, baby, look at his eyes.
This week he moppin' floors, next week is the fries. So...

Rap 4 Stick by his side.
I know this dude's ballin', and yeah, that's nice.
And they gon' keep callin' and tryin', but you stay right girl.
And when you get on, he leave your ass for a white girl.

Take A Bow

Words & Music by Mikkel Eriksen, Tor Erik Hermansen
& Shaffer Smith

Bust Your Windows

Words by Salaam Remi
Music by Salaam Remi & Jazmine Sullivan

1. I bust the win-dows out your car and, no, it did-n't mend my
(2.) car. You know I did it 'cause I

29

had to learn.___ I must ad-mit it helped a

played with it,___ ooh.___

lit-tle bit___ to think of how you'd feel when you saw it.___

I did-n't know that I had that much strength___ but___ I'm glad you see what

hap-pens when....___ You see you can't just play with peo ple's feel - ings,

tell them you love them and don't mean___ it. You'll prob-'ly say that it was

ju - ve - nile___ but___ I think that I de - serve to smile.___ Ha,___ I bust

1.
___ ha, ha,___ ha, ha. 2. I bust the win-dows out your But it don't com-pare to my

the win - dows out your car.

2.

bro - ken heart._____ You could nev - er feel how I

31

32

33

Oh, but why am I still cry-ing?

(Lead vocals ad lib. on repeat)

Why am I the one who's still cry - ing? Oh,___ oh,___

1.

___ you real - ly hurt me, ba - by. You real - ly,___ you real - ly hurt me, babe.

2.

I bust the win-dows out your car.

34

Taking Chances

Words & Music by Kara Dioguardi & David Stewart

Maybe you could show me how to try.
Maybe you could take me in, somewhere underneath your skin?
What do you say to taking chances? What do you say to jumping off the edge?
Never knowing if

Alone

Words & Music by Billy Steinberg & Tom Kelly

43

oh, _____ oh. _____ Till now _____ I al-ways got by _____ on my _____ own. _____

_____ I nev-er real-ly cared un-til I met you. And now it

chills me to the bone, how do I get _____ you a-lone? _____

1.

How do I get _____ you a-lone? _____

A - lone. _____ A -

- lone. _____

Maybe This Time

Words by Fred Ebb
Music by John Kander

Moderate swing ♩ = 95

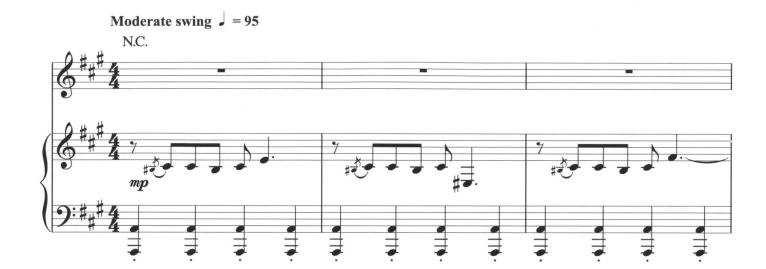

1. May-be this time I'll be luck-y,

may-be this time he'll stay.

A   Aaug

Somebody To Love

Words & Music by Freddie Mercury

down on my knees and I start to pray till the tears run down from my eyes, Lord,

some - bod - y, some - bod - y, can an - y - bod - y find me some - bod - y to
(Some - bod - y, some - bod - y.)

love?
(He works hard ev - 'ry day.)

Ev - 'ry___ day I

try and I try and I try,_____ but ev - 'ry-bod-y wants to put me down, they

say__ I'm go-in' cra - zy._____ They say I got a lot of wa-ter in my brain,_____ got

__ no com-mon sense._ I got no-bod-y left to be - lieve._____ Yeah,__ yeah,__ yeah,__ yeah.__

Instrumental Solo

Ooh, some-bod-y, some-bod-y, can an-y-bod-y find me some-

- bod-y to love?___

(An-y-bod-y___ find me___ some-one___ to

Got no

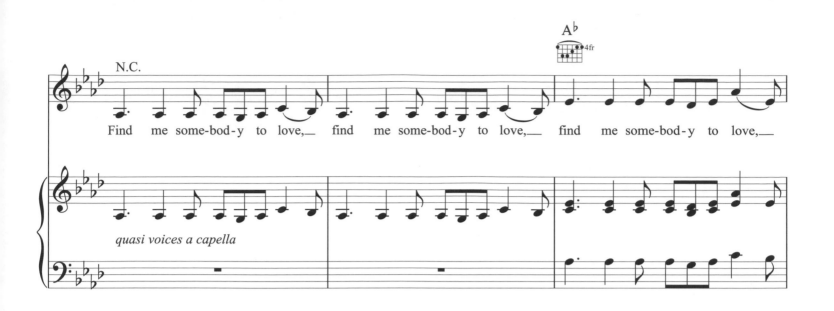

Find me some-bod-y to love,___ find me some-bod-y to love,___ find me some-bod-y to love,___

quasi voices a capella

find me some-bod-y to love,___ find me some-bod-y to love,___

find me some-bod-y to love,___ find me some-bod-y to love,___

find me some-bod-y to love._____ Find me some-bod-y to love,___

find me some-bod-y to love.____ Some-bod-y, some-bod-y, some-bod-y, some-bod-y,

some-bod-y, find me some-bod-y, find me some-bod-y to love. Can

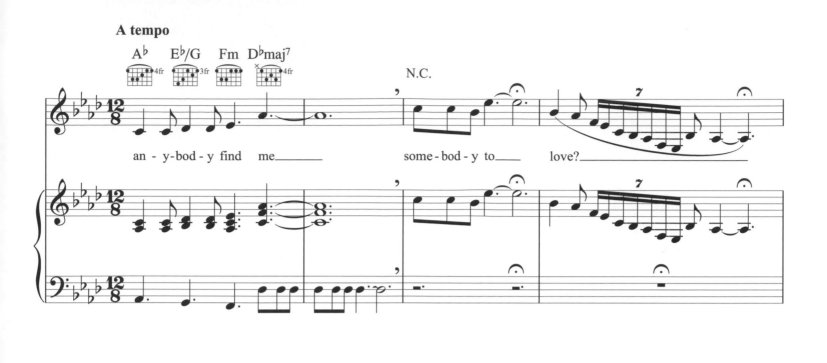

an-y-bod-y find me_____ some-bod-y to_____ love?_____

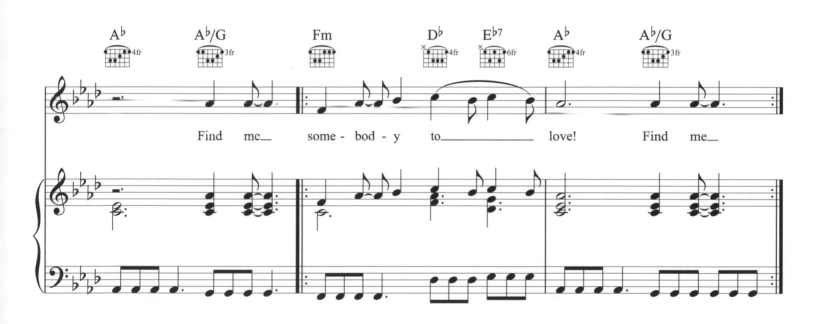

Find me__ some-bod-y to_____ love! Find me__

some-bod-y to_____ love! Find me, find me, find me, find me.

Hate On Me

Words & Music by Jill Scott, Adam Blackstone
& Steven McKie

and I don't feel no faults for all the lies that you bought.

You can try as you may, bring me down, but I say

that it ain't up to you, gon-na do what you do. Hate

on me, hat-er, now or lat-er, 'cause I'm gon-

Cm

Cm/B

- na do me. You'll be mad,____ ba - by.____ (Go 'head and hate.)_

Go 'head and hate on me, hat - er; I'm not a - fraid____

____ of____ what I got - ta pay____ for. (You can hate on me.)_ Ooh.__

____ 2. If I gave you peach - es out of my____ own gar - den,

and I made_ you a peach pie,___ would you slap me high?

Would you do it if I___ gave you dia - monds___ out of my_ own womb?

Would you feel the love_ in that, or ask, "Why not the moon?"

If___ I gave_ you san - i - ty for the whole of__ hu - man - i - ty,

had all___ the so - lu - tions___ for the pain___ and pol - lu - tion?___

Cm

No mat - ter where___ I live,___ de spite the things___ I give,___

Cm/B♭ **F(add²)/A**

you'll al - ways be this way,_____ so go a - head and hate___

Cm **Cm/B**

___ on me, hat - er,___ now___ or lat - er,___ 'cause I'm gon -

No Air

Words & Music by Harvey Mason, Damon Thomas,
James Fauntleroy, Erik Griggs & Steven Russell

Original key F♯ major

Moderately

how do you__ ex-pect me____ to live a-lone__ with just

me?__ 'Cause my world re-volves__ a-round you, it's__ so hard for me__ to breathe.__

Both: Tell me how I'm s'posed to breathe with no air.__ Can't live, can't breathe with no

air.__ That's how I feel when-ev-er you ain't there.__ There's no air, no air.__

Got me out here in the wa-ter so deep. Tell me how you gon'__ be with-out__

me? If you ain't here, I just can't breathe.__ There's no air, no air.__

No air,__ air, oh.__ No air,__ air, no.__

No air,__ air, oh. No air,__ air.

You Keep Me Hangin' On

Words & Music by Brian Holland, Eddie Holland
& Lamont Dozier

Original key A♭ major

Moderately fast

me hang - in' on.

You don't____ real - ly need____
Now you don't____ real - ly want____

me, but you keep____ me hang - in' on.
me, you just keep____ me hang - in' on.

1. Why do____ you keep a - com - in' a - round,____ play - in' a - with my heart?____
2. You say,____ al - though____ we broke____ up,____ you still wan - na be just friends.____

Why don't____ you get out____ of my life____
But how____ can____ we still____ be____ friends____ when

Keep Holding On

Words & Music by Avril Lavigne & Lukasz Gottwald

There's noth-ing you can say, noth-ing you can do. There's no oth-er way when it comes_ ___ to the truth___ so keep hold - ing on___ 'cause you know we'll make it through, we'll make it through. Hear me when I say, when I say I be - lieve that noth-in's gon-na change, noth-in's gon-na change des - ti - ny.___

Whatever's meant to be will work out perfectly, yeah, yeah,

yeah, yeah. La, da, da, da, la, da, da, da,

D.S. al Coda

la, da, da, da, da, da, da.

Keep holding on.

87

Bust A Move

Words & Music by Matt Dike, Marvin Young, Michael Ross,
Jim Walters & Luther Rabb

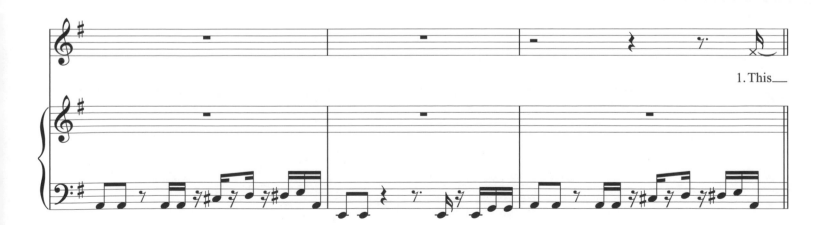

_here's a tale for all the fel-las try-in' to do what those la-dies tell us.
(2.) _ on a mis-sion and you're wish-in' some-one could kill your lone-ly con-di-tion.
(Verse 3 see block lyrics)

Get shot down 'cause you're o - ver zeal-ous. Play_ hard to get, fe - males get jea-lous.
Look-in' for love in all the wrong plac - es. No fine girls, just ug - ly fac - es.

O. K. smar-tie, go to a par - ty. Girls are scan - ti - ly clad_ and show-in' bod-y. A
From frus-tra-tion, first in-cli-na - tion is to be-come a monk and leave the sit-u-a-tion. But

chick walks by, you wish_ you could sex_ her but you're stand-in' on the wall like you_ was Poin-dex - ter.
ev - 'ry dark tun-nel has a light of hope so don't hang your-self with a cel-i - bate rope. Your

Drums

To Coda I ⊕

- by, you got it.
(Just bust a move.)_
If you___ want it,

you got it, oh, if you___ want it ba - by, you got it. Ah.

N.C.

In the cit - y la - dies look pret - ty. Guys tell jokes so they___ can seem wit - ty.

Tell a fun - ny joke just to get some play,_ then you try to make a move and she says "no way!"

Girls are fak - in', good-ness sak - in'. They want a man who brings home the ba - con.

Got no mon-ey and you got no car then you got no wom-an and there you are.__ Some

N.C.

girls are sa-dis - tic, ma - te - ri - al - ist - ic. Look-ing for a man makes 'em op-por-tun - is - tic. They

ly- in' on the beach per-pe-trat-in' a tan__ so that a broth-er with the mon-ey can be__ their man.__ So on the

beach you're stroll- in', real high roll - in'. Ev-'ry-thing you have is yours_ and not stol- en. A

D.S. al Coda

girl runs up with some-thin' to prove._ So don't just stand there, bust a move._

Coda I

N.C.

1.

Ah! Oh! Ah! Oh!

Drums

2.

Oh! Ah,____ hey,____ yeah,____ ah.____ Ah,_

ooh,_____ hey,_____ yeah,_____ ah,_____ ah,_____ hey,_____

D.S.S. al Coda II

yeah,_____ eeh,_____ ah._____ Ah._____ Ah._____ 3. Your

✛ *Coda II*

You_ want it,_____ you got it. Ah._____ You_ want it, ba -

1. - by you got it. Ah. **2.** - by you got it. Ah,_____ ah,___ ah,___

(Just bust a move.)

N.C.

hey.___ Ah,___ hah,___ yeah,___ ah.___ Hah,___ hey,___ hah,___

hey.___ Ah,___ hah,___ hey,___ yeah,___ yeah.___

Verse 3:
Your best friend Harry has a brother Larry
In five days from now he's gonna marry.
He's hopin' you can make it there if you can
'Cause in the ceremony you'll be the best man.

You say "neato", check your libido
And roll to the church in your new tuxedo.
The bride walks down just to start the wedding
And there's one more girl you won't be getting.

So you start thinkin', then you start blinkin'
A bride-maid looks and thinks that you're winkin'.
She thinks you're kinda cute so she winks back
And then you're feelin' really fine 'cause the girl is stacked.

Reception's jumpin, bass in pumpin'
Look at the girl, and your heart starts thumpin'.
Says she wants to dance to a different groove
Now you know what to do, G, bust a move.

Sweet Caroline

Words & Music by Neil Diamond

Original key C# major

Moderately, very steady

1. Where it be - gan,_

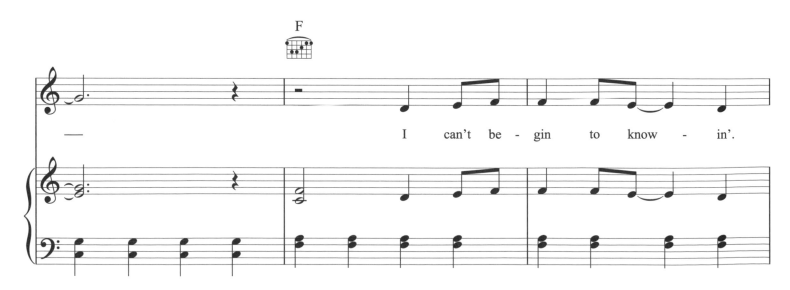

— I can't be - gin to know - in'.

But then I know it's grow-in' strong.

Was-n't the spring___ and spring be-came the sum-mer.___

Who'd have be-lieved___ you'd come a-long?

1. Hands,___ touch-in' hands,___
2. Warm,___ touch-in' warm,___

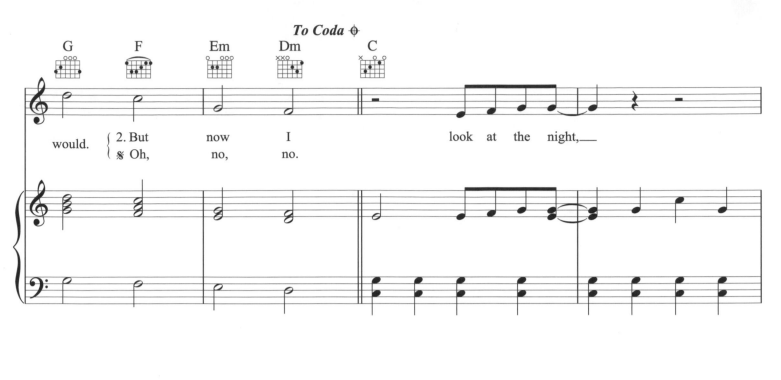

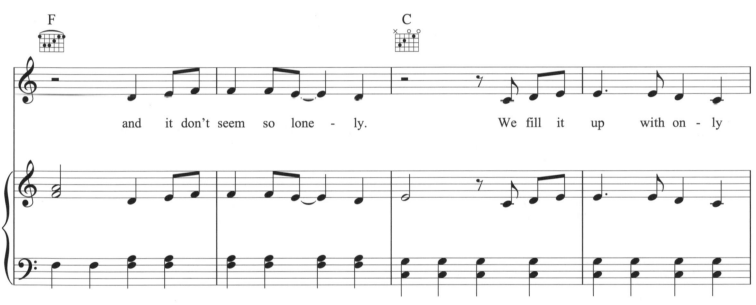

Sweet Car - o - line,___ good times nev - er seemed so

good._____ I've been in - clined___

to be - lieve___ they nev - er would._____ Sweet Car - o - line.

Dancing With Myself

Words & Music by Billy Idol & Tony James

Defying Gravity

Words & Music by Stephen Schwartz

1. Some-thing___ has changed with-in me, some-thing is___ not the same.
2. I'm through ac-cept-ing lim-its 'cause some-one says they're so.

I'm through with play-ing by___ the rules of___ some-one else-'s game.__
Some things I can-not change but till I try I'll nev-er know.__